Heroes of the Red Branch Knights

This story was adapted by author Ann Carroll
and illustrated by Derry Dillon

IRELAND'S BEST KNOWN STORIES
IN A NUTSHELL

Published 2014
by: In a Nutshell
an imprint of Poolbeg Press Ltd

123 Grange Hill, Baldoyle
Dublin 13, Ireland

Text © Poolbeg Press Ltd 2014

1

A catalogue record for this book is available from the British Library.

ISBN 978 1 84223 620 8

Cover design and illustrations by Derry Dillon
Printed by GPS Colour Graphics Ltd, Alexander Road, Belfast BT6 9HP

This book belongs to

- -

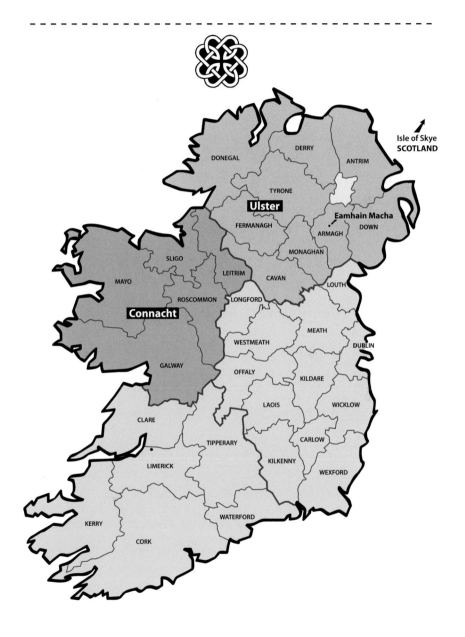

Also in the Nutshell series

How It All Began

One day Conor, King of Ulster, was sitting in his palace at Eamhain Macha. Having a bit of free time, he started thinking: I have a lot of gold and a fine palace, so I have lots of enemies. But if I want to be a really great king I need a proper army – not just men who'll fight and then go home, but brave warriors who will live here and defend me and what's mine to the death!

Plenty of young men wanted adventure and excitement at that time in Ulster. Conor picked the bravest for his army and they killed many of his enemies. Each of them got into the habit of bringing home the head of the man he'd killed and tying it to the branch of an oak tree outside the palace. Soon the branch was red with blood and that's how the young men came to be known as the Knights of the Red Branch.

Then Conor had another thought: My army is excellent but some of my warriors are bound to be killed and I'll need to replace them. I'll start a training camp for boys where they'll learn to be great fighters! That way there'll never be a shortage.

Then he had a further thought: My camp will also train boys from other parts of the country whose parents will pay for the privilege.

Conor was so pleased with these plans, he said to himself: "Really, I'm a very fine thinker. No wonder I'm king."

The Boys' Camp

Fergus Mac Roich was the King's right-hand man and Conor put him in charge of the Boys' Training Camp.

The youngest to join was Setanta, the king's nephew, who was seven and had great strength, speed and skill. Fergus fostered him in his own house, along with Conall Cernach of Ulster, and Ferdia of Connacht. The three boys became great friends.

They learned to use sword and shield in single combat, to throw a spear with deadly accuracy and drive a chariot at speed while wielding their weapons. They also learned to race silently through the forest and to take the enemy by surprise; and if they were faced with more than one enemy, to spot the weakest first, attack swiftly, and beat them all.

They also became hurlers and jousters and on sports days would play matches and compete in races and tournaments.

Cúchulainn and Ferdia

Soon after his arrival Setanta killed the great guard-dog of Culann the blacksmith. Seeing how upset the smith was, the boy promised, "I will take the place of your hound and guard your home until you train another dog as fierce as the one I've killed. And from now on my name will be Cúchulainn or the Hound of Culann."

Cúchulainn grew up to be Ireland's greatest hero. No one could beat him in a fair fight. He was the best warrior in the whole country – probably in the whole world.

In their early teens he and Ferdia went to the Isle of Skye in Scotland and trained with Scáthach, a powerful and famous woman warrior whose name meant 'Shadowy'. Among other skills she taught them to leap high into the air over their enemies and also how to fight underwater for a long time.

Before they left, Scáthach told them: "Ferdia, you are a great and powerful young warrior. You have proved again and again that ordinary weapons can't pierce your body, for your skin is as tough as armour. It is a powerful defence in battle to have such skin."

She turned then to Cúchulainn: "You are the
bravest and the best I've ever seen. Also you
have a clear head, good judgement and wisdom
beyond your years. Therefore it is to you I make
the gift of the Gae Bolg."

The Gae Bolg was a deadly spear against which there was no defence. It pierced both shield and armour. Once lodged in the body it opened into many spikes, causing agony and death.

Ferdia was delighted for his friend. "There's no one better than you," he told him. "You deserve such a fine weapon."

Training finished, they went home, Ferdia to Connacht and Cúchulainn to Ulster.

Conall and his Uncle Cet

Meanwhile their friend, Conall Cernach, was killing as many Connacht men as he could, even though he was half Connacht on his mother's side. At his birth, Cafad the Druid, who could see into the future, announced: "This child will grow up to kill many Connacht men."

"Then he shall not live!" said his Connacht uncle, Cet.

Snatching him from his mother's arms, Cet placed him on the ground and stood on his neck. His mother snatched him back immediately. But from then on, Conall had a crooked neck and a hatred for his uncle and for all Connacht men (except his childhood friend, Ferdia).

That's why he made it his business to kill as many as possible.

So his Uncle Cet swore, "Well then, to even things up I'll have to kill as many Ulstermen as possible!" And so he did.

Twice as Brainy

Cet also prided himself on stealing heads from
the head-branch at Eamhain Macha. One day
he took the petrified brain of Mesgegra, King
of Leinster. "It's like a rock but even harder!
I'll use it in my catapult."

Some time later he spotted King Conor and, taking his sling, he fired the brain and saw it lodge in Conor's forehead.

"Now you have two brains," he laughed, "though I don't think you'll be twice as brainy!"

(Conall eventually caught up on his Uncle Cet and killed him in single combat but was so badly wounded himself that he died a short time later.)

Of course Conor wasn't twice as brainy with two brains. He just had a lot of headaches.

"That brain can't be removed without killing you," the doctors told him. "But you'll be all right if you don't get excited!"

"All right? I'm not all right – my head is splitting! And I'm exceedingly ugly! Can you do nothing?"

"Well, we can tell you not to look at yourself and to stay calm."

For a long time Conor followed their advice. But one day, years later, it is said he learned of the death of Christ and got so angry Mesgegra's brain popped from his forehead and instantly he was dead.

The Sons of Usna

But long before that happened Conor had achieved his ambition of forming a great army. And three of his warriors who became famous in legend were Naoise, Ardal and Ainnle, the sons of Usna. They were champion fighters and fought hard for their king.

Then Naoise fell in love with Deirdre who was young and beautiful and loved him too. But the ageing Conor wanted her for his wife. Tragedy followed when she eloped with Naoise to Scotland. Ardal and Ainnle went with them but none of them could escape Conor's revenge.

The King tricked Fergus Mac Roich into bringing them all home, giving Fergus his word they would be safe. Once back in Ulster, Conor's army attacked them and, greatly outnumbered, the brothers died fighting.

Conor married Deirdre but in less than a year she was dead with grief.

Fergus and Maeve

Fergus was furious. "I will no longer serve a king who is so false!" he declared.

The great warrior went to Connacht where he fell in love with Queen Maeve and she with him. Unfortunately Maeve was married to Ailill, who wasn't a bit pleased at this turn of events.

"One day I'll kill Fergus!" Ailill vowed. "But Maeve is a ferocious woman and I don't want to anger her, so I have to be cunning."

The Queen was very beautiful and when she set her mind on something she usually got it. She set her mind on the Brown Bull of Cooley, a mighty animal belonging to Ulster, but he wasn't for sale.

So Maeve declared war and Fergus marched into Ulster by her side.

Defending Ulster

Cúchulainn was defending the ford into the province on his own, for all his comrades were under a sleeping spell. The enemy could advance only singly and Cúchulainn, in one to one combat, stood against them for days on end, killing all he fought.

When Fergus reached the ford and saw only his foster son, whom he loved, he didn't want to fight. Eventually he retreated with his forces.

But Ferdia too was with the Connacht army. He also didn't want to fight his old friend. Then Maeve called him a coward and goaded him into combat.

First the friends fought with equal weapons. Ferdia's armoured skin kept him safe. He was a great warrior and after a long hard contest managed to wound Cúchulainn.

"This is no fair fight!" Cúchulainn was
furious and, taking the Gae Bolg, launched it
with mighty speed at his best friend. The effect
was terrible. The spear-head drove into Ferdia's
chest, opened into barbs, and he sank to his
knees in agony.

Badly hurt himself, Cúchulainn went to his friend immediately. "We should never have fought," he mourned. "We were the best of comrades. Now we've each caused the other's death."

Ferdia died in great pain and Cúchulainn, much weakened and fearing for Ulster, tied himself upright to a tree, his weapons ready.

Cúchulainn's Death

None of the enemy approached, for they knew how Ferdia had died and were afraid. Cúchulainn's eyes closed and his head dropped. Still they waited. A raven settled on the warrior's shoulder and so they knew for sure he was dead. Only then did they advance.

But by now the Red Branch Knights had woken from the spell. They defeated Maeve's army, but not before she had captured the Brown Bull and brought it back to Connacht.

Fergus Mac Roich returned with Maeve to Connacht. The Queen's husband, Ailill, was fiercely jealous and one day tracked them into the forest. Hearing their laughter and mad with rage, he got a blind archer to fire at Fergus, pretending it was a deer he wanted killed. Fergus had no chance.

Aftermath

For some years after Conor's reign his army continued to exist. But the greatest were dead. Then the training camp closed and, in time, the warriors disbanded.

The Knights lived nearly two thousand years ago yet their deeds have passed into legends that are still told and Cúchulainn, brave and fearless, is a national hero.

He inspired many and his statue stands in the
GPO in Dublin, a reminder of his short life and
heroic death, as well as a symbol of the 1916
Easter Rising.

The End

Word Sounds

(Opinions may differ regarding pronunciation)

Words	Sounds
Roich	Ro-ick
Setanta	Set-ant-a
Cernach	Ker-nock
Ferdia	Fer-dee-ah
Cuchullainn	Coo–cull-an
Scathach	Sca-hock
Cet	Ket
Eamhain	Ow-an ('ow' rhymes with 'how')
Macha	Mocka
Mesgegra	Mess-geg-rah
Usna	Us-nah
Naoise	Neesha
Ailill	Al-ill

Also available from the **IN A NUTSHELL** series
All you need to know about Ireland's best loved stories in a nutshell

The Story of Newgrange

The Salmon of Knowledge

The Story of Saint Patrick

How Cúchulainn Got His Name

The Children of Lir

The Story of The Giant's Causeway

Granuaile The Pirate Queen

Oisín and Tír na nÓg

The Story of Brian Boru

Deirdre of the Sorrows

If you enjoyed this book from
Poolbeg why not visit our website:

www.poolbeg.com

and get another book delivered straight
to your home or to a friend's home.

All books despatched within 24 hours.

POOLBEG

Why not join our mailing list
at www.poolbeg.com and get some
fantastic offers, competitions,
author interviews and much more?

@PoolbegBooks